HANNE TÜRK

# DO IT YOURSELF MAX

HI FI
TV
RADIO-
SERVICE

5412.20

TV
RADIO-SERVICE

HIFI
TV
RADIO-
SERVICE

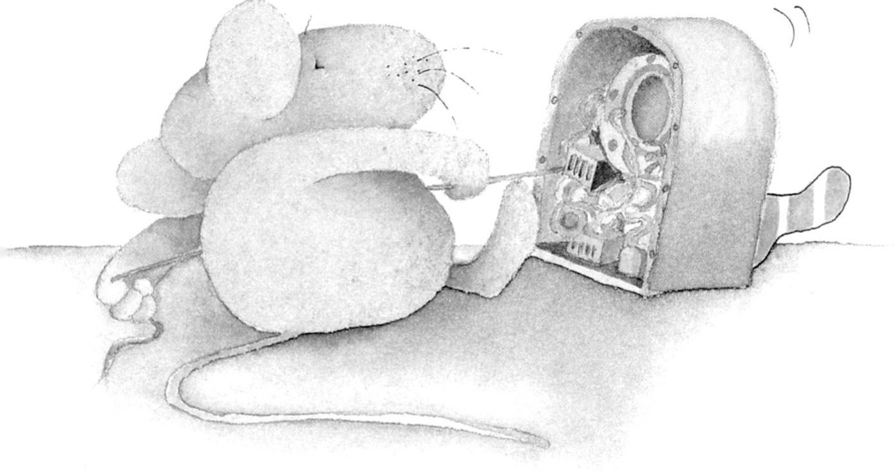

**THE MORE MAX THE MERRIER!**

1 A SURPRISE FOR MAX
2 MAX VERSUS THE CUBE
3 THE ROPE SKIPS MAX
4 A LESSON FOR MAX
5 RAINY DAY MAX
6 MAX THE ART LOVER
7 MERRY CHRISTMAS MAX
8 RAKING LEAVES WITH MAX
9 GOODNIGHT MAX
10 MAX PACKS
11 SNAPSHOT MAX
12 HAPPY BIRTHDAY MAX
13 BUTTERFLY MAX
14 GOOD SPORT MAX
15 FRIENDSHIP MAX
16 CHOCOLATE MAX
17 ROBINSON MAX
18 BON APPÉTIT MAX
19 A FRIGHT FOR MAX
20 DO IT YOURSELF MAX
\+ MAX CARDS
\+ MAX PLUSH TOYS
\+ MAX CALENDARS
\+ MAX POSTERS

FIND THEM AT YOUR LOCAL
BOOKSTORE OR GIFTSHOP.